Cultiv

Doula Heart

Cultivating the Doula Heart

Essentials of Compassionate Care

Francesca Lynn Arnoldy

Contemplative Doula, LLC
(802) 578-2458
Contemplativedoula.com

ISBN-13: 978-1-7327806-0-6

Cover photography and design by
Francesca Lynn Arnoldy
Author photo by North Photography, LLC

The advice and strategies found within may not be
suitable for every situation. This work is sold with the
understanding that neither the author nor the publisher
are held responsible for the results accrued from the
advice in the book.

To my dearest dears, Hays and Maeven. You are kismet embodied. I cannot begin to imagine two beings more perfectly suited to inspire my innermost hope, dedication, and love for this life of mine. To be blessed with your presence required the grace of fate and the bonds of many—none more appreciated than yours, Veronica, relentlessly selfless and doting mother of mine; and yours, John Paul, my love—I'm so glad we chose each other and continue to do so.

Table of Contents

Foreword

We are living in an epidemic of loneliness. A recent survey of more than twenty thousand adults living in the United States finds that most are lonely and only 1 in 5 feel that they have a person to talk to.[1] Britain recently appointed a new Minister of Loneliness to address the nearly nine million people in the UK who feel isolated — two hundred thousand of whom are elders who report not having had a conversation with a friend or family member in more than a month.[2]

In my role as a palliative care physician, I find that loneliness might be the single greatest source of suffering that seriously ill people encounter in our modern world. In his landmark 1982 New England Journal of Medicine article, Dr. Eric Cassel defines suffering as "being experienced by persons, not merely bodies, and has its source in challenges that threaten the intactness of the person as a complex social and psychological entity."[3] In some situations, we can reduce or eliminate the things that are hurting us (e.g., physical sources of pain, nausea, anxiety). Sometimes, however, these can be harder to ameliorate (e.g., regret and shame, loss, existential

---

[1] https://www.multivu.com/players/English/8294451-cigna-us-loneliness-survey/docs/FactSheet_1524071393425-302762795.pdf

[2] https://www.nytimes.com/2018/01/17/world/europe/uk-britain-loneliness.html

[3] Cassel E. (1982). The Nature of Suffering and the Goals of Medicine. *New England Journal of Medicine*. 306(11):639-45.

terror). However, as Cassel helps us see, hurt is not synonymous with suffering. It is the sense of an impending or completed loss of personhood that causes us to suffer. In my experience being with people who are suffering, the perceived loss of personhood happens most often when the person whose body and mind are being hurt also feels isolated, stigmatized, abandoned and, ultimately, unknown for the person they wish others to see. Sometimes, suffering is intensely resistant to the things I, as a physician and person, know how to do or ways to be. However, I am reminded daily that our most effective clinical tool for alleviating suffering is our interest in being fully present, of fearlessly bearing witness, of curiously wanting to know the person and, sometimes, merely offering space to laugh about the sheer craziness of it all.

This book captures the wisdom of the Doula about what it means to be fully present with those who are often lonely and suffering. The teachings here can help each of us learn to turn toward suffering and, maybe, make space for a twinkle of joy.

Bob Gramling M.D., D.Sc.
Holly and Bob Miller Chair in Palliative Medicine
University of Vermont

Wording and Grammar Choices

They/Them/Their will be used throughout the book as plural and/or singular gender-neutral pronouns to respect non-binary expressions of identity.

Doula is an ancient Greek word that loosely translates to a woman who serves women. At present, we recognize the term more broadly to refer to caregivers who provide nonmedical, emotional support to those facing major life transitions such as birth and death.

Due to my deep, humble reverence for doula work, I have borrowed numerous terms that are often associated with organized religions, such as *devout*, *bless*, *sacred*, *faith*, etc. This book has no specific religious alignment or affiliation. However, there are a few references to pragmatic approaches from secular Buddhism and one reference to the "Golden Rule."

"Soul" is a term chosen to represent that which lies at the core of our humanity where we are inextricably connected and united in the universal absolutes of suffering, joy, pain, and love. It does not refer to an aspect of our being which may (or may not) exist before or after our physical body dies.

Prelude to the Work

My initiation into the realm of end-of-life support presented itself unexpectedly when my grandfather was dying. I showed up largely unprepared for what I was walking into, which is the case for all doula work, honestly. We don't know exactly what will be asked of us or how we'll help ahead of time. My grandmother was exhausted and happily handed over his care to me so she could sleep. This would be my first time sitting vigil through someone's death. I stepped in and stepped up, having had no real preparation—no studies, no trainings, and barely any frame of reference. Heart in hand, I began my *work*.

My grandfather, curled in a fetal position, was already in a deep coma sleep, so he was verbally uncommunicative. His feeble state and arrhythmic inhalations begged the questions: *How are you still alive? And, why?*

I sat by his side in that quiet house, reading a book that was coincidentally perfect for calming my nerves. It happened to contain his favorite prayer, "Make me an Instrument of your Peace," which spoke volumes to me about what it means to be "of service." I communicated with my grandfather on a spiritual level with comforting words. He slept, didn't move, and rarely breathed. I was sure he was working, though. And it seemed like hard work. Mysterious work. He was working through something... working on something... working toward something. I encouraged his efforts and held him in peace and love.

For his wife and three children (one of whom hadn't been able to visit for the previous week or so because it was too upsetting, and one of whom waited until the final breaths to enter the room), it was excruciating to get through this period as it continued on, much the same, the next morning. I took notice of their discomfort, but I didn't share their sentiment. Because of my birth work, I felt comfortable with the unknown, intrigued by it, an eager student of it. This is what death asks of doulas: *Can we settle into this liminal space?*

We seem to afford birth more ups and downs than death while still calling it "beautiful." But birth is also arduous work ("labor"). It beckons all of a woman's strength, determination, and belief. We puke, we have diarrhea, we have flashbacks of abuse and trauma, we scream, we beg for it to end, we moan like animals, we bite on things, we cry. Not always, not all of it, not for everyone every time, but these responses are normal aspects of the process, and yet birth is still "beautiful." And it is.

Can death be beautiful, too? Can we hold steady through the twists and turns? Can we support with compassion? Can we *doula*? I say, yes. Not without apprehension or doubts. That isn't reasonable. We can with trust—trust in the humanity that lives in our core, trust in our inner wisdom and benevolent intentions. We can, with the unwavering, prevailing courage of the doula heart.

Introduction

Years ago, during a time of vocational vacillation, a seasoned birth worker assured me that I had (what she called) the "doula heart." She saw in me what I hadn't yet recognized. She nudged me forward and gave me the confidence to launch my private practice, Vermont Birth Haven. Since then, I have found myself returning to this concept of the doula heart. Never has it been so present in my thoughts as while developing and facilitating the University of Vermont Larner College of Medicine's End-of-Life Doula Professional Certificate Program. My task was to translate beginning-of-life support skills into those needed at end-of-life.

There are many similarities between the two realms. There's the palpable mix of undulating unknowns and knowns. There's the gentle fading away of time as we usually experience it. The mysterious unfolding of both birth and death is poised to cause confusion, leaving people in the throes feeling overwhelmed and helpless.

Of course, there are also a few marked differences between the two bookends of life, the most evident being the outcome. Birth generally ends with the celebration of a new life. Death ends with the grief of a life ended. To ensure the university's training program was comprehensive, I needed to determine what is at the center of doula care.

Cultivating the Doula Heart is the culmination of my contemplation. It's an overview born of exploration, grappling with long-held assumptions, and pondering quietly. It's a compilation of insights and lessons learned from the subject matter experts and students of the course as well as the clients and loved ones I've had the honor of supporting.

This concise written work is part guidebook, part impassioned plea. My hope is to inspire confidence and resolve, encouraging people to heed the call to compassionate action. Whether you're a doula, medical care provider, librarian, or geologist, you will experience loss and you will witness others experiencing loss.

Do you feel ready and willing to step closer and become a shoulder to lean on? Can you find ease in the midst of pregnant pauses? Can you remain present in the face of another's suffering without succumbing to discomfort yourself? Do you worry about what to say and how to offer help? This book can assuage these common fears.

The doula heart can be infused into all work and into any relationship. As you read this book, keep what resonates and consider what doesn't. Implement and integrate the information and approaches that are useful and beneficial to your life and work.

Doula work is an active practice. A contemplative practice. A lifelong practice (I anticipate). Cultivating the doula heart requires energy, focus, and intention.

All are welcome.

SECTION ONE

Essentials of Doula Care

Providing emotional support is the main task of a doula. Careful attention to the inner well-being of clients is present in every word, touch, approach, and technique utilized. In our work, doulas believe in people. We believe in life and the mysterious enigma of death. We aspire to promote people's sense of agency and growth through deep listening and personalized, nonjudgmental care. Doulas are reverent allies. We align ourselves compassionately with the goals, wishes, and needs of each client. We normalize and clarify. Quite simply, doulas care—in the most wholehearted, unconditional interpretation of the term, understanding and respecting the basic need to connect as we behold the full range of emotions and experiences.

Doulas recognize beauty in the complete expression of our humanness, in the work of dying and in the act of witnessing death.

D - Dedication to Presence

O - Open-Mindedness

U - Understanding with Compassion

L - Listening Intently

A - Allaying Distress

Dedication to Presence:
Vessel of calm, well of trust

*"There's a morning when presence
comes over your soul. You sing like a
rooster in your earth-colored shape.
Your heart hears and, no longer frantic,
begins to dance."*
-Rumi

Doulas practice the art of holding space. We create a safe atmosphere in which people can feel their feelings, express themselves, and work through issues with authenticity and courage. This holding has the soft warmth of an embrace, encouraging rather than stifling. As we develop rapport with clients, they come to trust our nonjudgmental approach to care. They feel valued, and therefore allow themselves to be vulnerable.

We find abundant spaciousness within this space we hold. There's room for it all—joy and sorrow, laughter and tears, wonderment and worry. We invite any of it in and let it be present, watching shifts and changes emerge. Things don't need to be a certain way. Humans are complicated beings capable of a complicated array of emotion.

This is a space of non-duality. Living and dying aren't opposites. We're living right up until the moment we die. We're able to make memories, convey affection and disapproval, and have ups and downs. There's space for being in our heads, being in our bodies, and being in our hearts. We can be present in moments while holding an overarching acknowledgment of our mortality in the backdrop.

Doulas are emotionally and physically present to silently witness, gently validate, and accept another's choices. We hold people's information and experiences in confidence, and we hold their truth with reverence. We are holders, though, not keepers. There is no clinging. We know our client's journey is not ours. We carry forward any wisdom we've gained without a sense of responsibility for determining another person's way of living and dying.

Doulas honor the value of togetherness, of being with another, and of "non-doing." However, we are not passive. We are actively fostering inner peacefulness and quiet in order to be fully attentive. We are active in our being. Doulas remain focused on our clients (with a soft gaze), cultivating an intentional presence by upholding connection and remaining centered. When our thoughts meander, we consciously return to the moment, anchoring ourselves in the present.

Distractions can emerge internally or from external sources (e.g., brainstorming what to cook for dinner or hearing a television program blaring in the room next door). We remain vigilant and mindful, knowing that our attentiveness has a direct effect on our client's perception. Whenever needed, we breathe and re-center. A doula might engage a mantra or breath word to accomplish this practice. For example: "present" on the inhale, "still" on the exhale. Certain words, phrases, poems, or blessings might come directly from clients, and we may be inspired to adopt their language to provide the most individualized support.

Often we are silent witnesses, humble and devout in our doula practice. Doulas enter into the most poignant life and death moments, and we are remembered for our role in the hearts and minds of those who live on. It is an honor to be invited into this realm, complex as it can become. We acknowledge that the emotional responses of our clients and their surrounding caregivers and visitors will not always be peaceful. If a crisis mounts, doulas do not escalate calamity by matching stress with distress. We remain calm and steady in our resolve to support those in need of care.

Open-Mindedness:
If you've supported one loss, you've supported one loss

> *"In the beginner's mind there are many possibilities, but in the expert's there are few."* -Shunryo Suzuki

Doulas recognize universal themes in the human experience. However, instead of allowing these commonalities to become assumptions, we invite them to inform our ability to normalize and validate clients' experiences, providing much-needed comfort. We assure people: *You are not alone in this feeling.*

People are more alike than unalike, and yet, doulas must also honor each person's uniqueness. Doulas practice with open minds and open hearts. We adopt a "beginner's mind."

Comprehensive training, study, and work in the field can help doulas build a strong foundation of knowledge— and yet we will never be death experts. We are students of death and students of our clients—always learning and expanding the perimeters of our grasp. By nature, death is mysterious. We can generate guesses and theories, but we are without certainty. Uncertainty can inspire fear or curiosity. We have a choice as to how we respond.

Can we listen as our clients wonder and ponder without feeling the need to explain the inexplicable? Can we pose unanswerable questions to encourage clients to explore the outer regions of understanding? Can we support what our clients believe without attachment to our own beliefs (or lack thereof)? Can we put aside our yearning for control and management to surrender to the greatest of unknowns?

With open minds, doulas meet people where they are in their journey. We hold no expectations about where this should start or end. We are accepting of clients whether they are embracing their imminent death or denying it completely. We know that people need an *emotion ally* during these times, not someone who attempts to drag them through the experience, pleading and pushing. We extend a standing invitation for clients to discover their full potential for growth and awareness, at their pace.

Understanding with Compassion:
At all times, people are whole and intact

*"Compassion is not a relationship
between the healer and the wounded.
It's a relationship between equals. Only
when we know our own darkness well
can we be present with the darkness of
others. Compassion becomes real when
we recognize our shared humanity."*
-Pema Chödrön

From a soul's eye view, doulas understand suffering as inevitable and expected. It is an uninvited visitor throughout each of our lives. Through training and practice, doulas engage in introspective work to explore past hurts, regrets, shame, guilt, and loss so as to be emotionally available to clients. We uncover our own unresolved issues, baggage, and triggers so that we can differentiate what's ours and what's our client's.

We face our own mortality with as much authenticity as possible. We accept suffering as universal. We acknowledge pain. We see its many forms—spiritual, physical, and psychological. In response, we cultivate deep compassion. To know compassion, we can start by delineating sympathy and empathy.

What is Sympathy?

"I feel sad/bad for you."

Sympathizing means feeling sorry for someone. It means conjuring up an emotional state of pity in response to someone else's difficult experience. We take on a feeling that wasn't organically ours when we sympathize. We might even feel guilty for remaining neutral or positive in our own hearts while someone else is suffering. By sharing in sorrow, we believe we are bonding. We commiserate; yet by doing so, we compound challenging situations by adding in our own emotions.

What is Empathy?

"I feel how this feels for you."

Empathizing means taking one step back from sympathy by attempting to envision how we would feel if in the other person's shoes. Or, we remember how we have felt in a similar circumstance. We think we are meeting someone where they're at by overlaying our imagined experience onto their reality or our past onto their present. This responsive feeling can't exactly match another person's, as this is not possible. Emotions are fluid and personal and unique.

Sympathy and empathy, while well-intentioned approaches to offering solace, can be draining. Instead of being fully available to support another, we are expending energy as we feel sad for someone or attempt to feel what they're enduring. Trying to match our emotional landscape to that of another can be exhausting.

When we enter into compassion, however, we transition from the Golden Rule ("do unto others as you would have them do unto you") to the Platinum Rule (coined by Dr. Milton Bennett in the 1970s): "Do unto others as they would have done unto them."

What is Compassion?

"I honor how this feels for you."

Compassion moves beyond empathy. Its horizons are vast, its vantage broad. Compassion means learning how someone feels by becoming a neutral ally and witness. We make no assumptions. We do not guess. We "allow" others their emotions by conveying our acceptance, and we give them adequate space (safe and boundless) to explore these feelings for themselves.

Simultaneously, we recognize our shared humanity in the common conditions of pain and suffering. As a fellow human, we know pain. We know suffering. What we do not claim to know is how another person views and manages these hardships. When we create room between what's "mine" and what's "yours," we find that this slight detachment leads to more genuine connection because the bond is not based on our effort to harbor shared misery.

Doulas do not dip into internal reserves to replenish a client's sense of emptiness. Instead, a doula believes in the intactness of each human being and their limitless potential to evolve, all while holding them in unconditional positive regard. We recognize the tendency toward self-doubt during times of intensity and firmly believe in people's capacity to find their footing and next steps, even—especially—when they feel lost or overwhelmed.

Doulas can become the antidote (not the answer) to toxic stress by embodying unfaltering trust in every person's inherent wisdom and strength. We encourage a thoughtful slowing down when many feel rushed to get past a hurdle. We nurture contemplation as clients consider tumultuous questions and confusion. We turn toward and lean into suffering with our abiding faith in people.

The courageous exploration of what's most hidden illuminates understanding. Our speculation about a seemingly terrifying prospect tends to be much more exaggerated than the reality of it. Doulas can inquire gently and leave pauses for pondering, while demonstrating genuine interest. We are loyal allies, meaning we will not retreat and cower. We rise up to meet turmoil with confidence in our client's ability to travel through the murk and come out the other side with newfound fortitude. Doulas welcome the discomfort found in liminal space—the space between. It is through the struggle that each of us finds our compass and, ultimately, our truest sense of self.

Doulas recognize each client's limitless potential for transformation. Through our regard for their innate wholeness, clients are invited to see it for themselves. We are not in the business of rescuing. We do not save others from their experiences. We do not fix anyone or their problems. People are entitled to the completeness of their journeys. We can trust clients with hardship as we companion them on their journeys.

Practicing compassion, as such, energizes and revitalizes us. We provide support without depleting ourselves. We feel hopeful, not fatigued. This becomes a mutually generative exchange between doula and client.

Listening Intently:
Honoring the client's word as testimony

> *"There is a way between voice and*
> *presence, where information flows.*
> *In disciplined silence it opens;*
> *with wandering talk it closes."* -Rumi

Just as we are active in our presence, we are active in our listening. As clients peel back layers of emotional protection, expose "flaws," and drop their guard, we enter into our supportive role as listener. Doulas do not condone, condemn, or acquit. We remain impartial. We listen without judgment.

We tune into complete messages being shared, beyond the mere words spoken. We ensure our clients feel heard, validated, supported, and not abandoned. We assure: *What you say is legitimate. You are entitled to your voice.*

The art of listening includes practicing mindfulness. Instead of formulating responses as someone is speaking, we remain present and attentive, allowing for silence and additional opportunity for expression. Doulas become mirrors, reflecting and rewording to aid the process of clarification. We ask to hear more, especially when we notice heightened emotion surrounding certain topics. We redirect when a client wants to shift the focus toward us, allowing for rapport to be built through our sincere engagement, not through the over-sharing of our personal lives.

For humans to make sense of the world, we organize incoming information by categorizing. It's natural for people to mentally place one another into groups. If doulas tell clients about a religious practice (or lack thereof), political affiliation, or any other potentially polarizing belief system, we will wear that label from then on in their eyes. This can close doors of communication. Clients might hold back for fear of offending us. Or, if there's a common belief, a client might jump to conclusions about our view on related topics, assuming we have the exact same lens.

Our neutrality forges a safe, reliable base. Rather than focusing on the doula, a client relates to their own experience. We encourage introspection and processing aloud. The client can speak freely without fear of ridicule or minimization. Doulas are not aloof in our presence or responses, however. With compassion infused into active listening, we honor all that a client discloses with calmness and a kind countenance.

As clients communicate pain, trauma, anxieties, or secrets, we sustain the "strong back, soft front" that end-of-life pioneer Joan Halifax calls "the relationship between equanimity and compassion." She explains, "'Strong back' is equanimity and your capacity to really uphold yourself. 'Soft front' is opening to things as they are."

Allaying Distress:
Providing consciously anodyne support

Anodyne: Not likely to offend or arouse tensions.[4]
Anodyne: Capable of soothing or eliminating pain.[5]

Doulas do not offend. We are anodyne in our neutrality. Our presence is non-anxious and innocuous. We offer support without drawing attention to ourselves. This is not ego work; this is heart work. While supporting clients, we become caregiving chameleons. There's shape-shifting involved. There's the need to read the room.

Who's stressed? Who's quiet? What's missing? What can I introduce that would best honor my client? How can I promote ease and decrease stress?

Doulas enable people to operate within their comfort zones, filling in gaps as they arise. We step in or step back according to the needs of the moment. We do our work humbly and seek no glory. We remain camouflaged in the background, quietly empowering others.

In being of service, we want clients to attribute their triumphs to themselves—their victories, their pride. We do not want people to become dependent on our

---

[4] Anodyne [Def. 2]. (n.d.). Merriam-Webster Online. Retrieved July 18, 2018 from https://www.merriam-webster.com/dictionary/anodyne.

[5] Anodyne [Def. 1]. (n.d.) *American Heritage® Dictionary of the English Language, Fifth Edition*. (2011). Retrieved July 18, 2018 from https://www.thefreedictionary.com/anodyne.

presence or our care. Clients are not indebted to doulas. Instead, we assure: *You are not powerless. You have all you need, in you and surrounding you.* Doula work is an act of sacred altruism.

When we enter into a client's space, we set the intention for their "greatest good," knowing that any guesses we might make about what is best could be misguided or short-sighted. In our doula hearts, we wish for clients to maintain holistic health, as per their definition of that. Our overarching goals include reinforcing self-advocacy and lessening the chances the client will be traumatized (or re-traumatized) by their experience.

Doulas can become that which is lacking for a client. To orchestrate equanimity, doulas manifest soul-to-soul resonance in our connection. We radiate what each client seeks. When there's stress, we are calm. When there's anger, we are kind. When there's loneliness, we become an *emotion ally.* We do not attempt to sway a client away from what they are feeling, though. We make a conscious effort not to be swept along in the current. Doulas don't escalate.

We are sensitive and affirming, soothing in our care. We are not dismissive. We do not minimize a person's interpretation of what they are undergoing. Through all the ways we doula, we promote empowerment and healing born of processing and bravely facing that which threatens one's sense of intactness. This healing—not in the sense of a cure, but in the sense of an unbroken soul—generates peace in the face of chaos.

SECTION TWO

Before, During, and After Loss:
A Doula's Place in Sacred Space

Although there is no neat, orderly timeline or trajectory for grieving, there are some common components that dying people and their loved ones face. Reviewing them helps us understand common responses and the upheaval caused by loss.

Initially, people often experience shock and disbelief. Facing a major loss can be too overwhelming for the psyche to handle all at once. This is normal and an important protective feature of coping.

"This can't be true." "There must be some mistake."

At other times, people feel upset and even cheated by life (or their religion or beliefs) and angry about their diagnosis. Expressing feelings of unfairness, outward blame, and even rage actually creates an opening for beginning to accept what is happening, because the individual is moving beyond denial.

"Why me?" "How can this be happening?" "Life is so unfair."

The desire to make deals with the universe, deities, religious figures, or other people can also arise. These negotiations and promises are steeped in emotional uncertainty.

"If I start living better, can I be granted a cure?" "If I beat this cancer, I'll do more charity work."

Sadness is very common. People can settle into dark places and be consumed with sorrow as they grapple with impending loss. Accepting the unwanted reality of the situation might make people feel hopeless and helpless.

"How can I go on living like this?" "What's the point?"

Generally, with time, individuals begin to integrate the news into their sense of self and into their new normal. There can be glimpses of peacefulness, and then an unraveling once more. Feelings of acceptance can ebb and flow.

"This is hard, but I think I can handle it." "How might I spend the time I have left in ways that are meaningful and fulfilling?"

Doulas support both the dying person and their loved ones. In the spirit of non-judgment, a doula respects this winding traverse. The components of grief aren't good or bad, wrong or right. They just are. And doulas meet people where they are as they vacillate. A doula becomes a reliable buoy as clients encounter undulating waves of distress and serenity.

Aspects of Loss

Progressionary

Grief is generally layered and gradual, and thus, so are people's responses. This aspect of loss is often referred to as "anticipatory" — yet "progressionary" seems more apt. A terminal diagnosis is often accompanied by a progression of decline and a cascade of smaller losses. These include independence, abilities, roles, and the sense of control over one's life. Often what has held most significance will be the hardest to let go. Progressionary grief includes mourning the incremental losses as they arise, and continually re-acclimating. Another aspect is preparing for the major loss by conceiving plans (for before and after), finding closure, and meaning-making (processing). People facing death picture life continuing on without them. Their loved ones attempt to visualize surviving the loss.

It's important to note that the root word of "progressionary" is "progress." In the midst of loss and sadness, there is room for hope, growth, and healing. We're living right up until the moment we die. It's possible to find peace, reconcile differences, and sort priorities. Not all the time. Not in everyone's experience. Yet, there's potential for progress. We can continue to become our best selves and know our own strength even when faced with the hardest thing. As doulas, we acknowledge how rich and fluctuating each person's experience will be. Life (and death) aren't static.

Loss

As people face major loss, care needs intensify. Energy is taxed. Feelings run the gamut. Some hang on, some let go, and some feel ready. Some loved ones (when available) want to thoroughly participate in caregiving; others retreat into solitude. Some people wish to die consciously and aware; others request heavy sedation. There's stress, there's love, there's togetherness, there's isolation, there's despair. Each death is different. Family dynamics are magnified and potentially threatened. Arguably, there's no greater turbulence.

Mourning

In the acute period following major loss, loved ones usually fluctuate between shock, despair, and sadness. Numbness, anguish, tears, changes in eating and sleeping habits, as well as decreased energy levels and ability to "function" are all possible. The bereaved may feel relief that pain or suffering has ended, gratefulness for time shared, and a sense of celebration of the life honored. Additionally, primary caregivers often feel lost as their responsibilities abruptly end with the death of their loved one. They also grieve any roles they held in relation to the person who died (e.g., spouse, child, uncle, sibling, etc).

The Way of the Doula

Ways of BEING

- Emotion ally
- Meeting people where they are
- Turning toward suffering
- Maintaining a beginner's mind
- Companioning and serving
- Intentional presence
- Compassion
- Non-judgment
- Non-agenda
- Unconditional positive regard

Ways of DOING

- Discovering a client's wishes
- Working through a client's fears/anxieties
- Honoring and holding sacred space
- Leading guided imagery, visualizations, and breathing exercises
- Promoting informed consent
- Assisting with legacy and completion work, as well as advance directives
- Conducting life review sessions
- Providing resource referrals
- Coordinating care
- Vigil planning and sitting

During each visit, a doula's time is determined by what's most pressing for the client, and depends on each doula's specific range of offerings.

Is it developing rapport?

A doula earns a client's trust by becoming a steady, reliable figure during a time of unpredictability. We enter into a client's space with our doula hearts primed to serve. Clients come to count on doulas as confidants. As we move past friendly banter, we open space for earnest exploration of wishes and anxieties. "What is most worrisome?" we ask in a number of ways without the expectation of providing solutions. As an ally, a doula walks alongside, even through the difficult terrain.

Is it rest?

A doula can sit in silence, becoming a "protective presence" in a client's space. Some doulas might offer respite as part of their care package, giving loved ones time away for self-care or running errands. We recognize that increased sleepiness is a natural, anticipated aspect of the body's journey. Doulas remain actively engaged, even when sitting as quiet witness. We might read silently or aloud from a book that is meaningful to the client. We might write in a client's journal if they choose to have a collective record of notes and updates from their team and visitors. We recognize that even during times of rest, clients are working on this path toward death. When bedside, we remain aware of our calmness and always set the intention for each client's "greatest good."

Is it a task?

A doula might be willing to fold laundry, wash dishes, stack a pile of firewood, weed a flowerbed, or arrange a client's space for ease of visits. This can lift a significant burden off the shoulders of the client and their loved ones, easing stress and anxiety. If a task falls outside of our specific offerings, we can explore additional options, ensuring needs are met. When people facing a terminal diagnosis feel they have more to accomplish, it can prevent them from feeling at peace. Doulas invite serenity into the forefront. If we can assist with checking off items on their to-do list, we can uncover the remaining tasks that hold more weight.

Is it guided meditation?

Relaxation, breathing, visualization, and imagery exercises aim to lower stress and re-center a person. Doulas can use basic scripts or play recordings for clients, perhaps with soothing background music or nature sounds. We can lead a client into a progressive relaxation and then ask them to think of the most comforting, safe place they've ever visited. Once there, we invite them to explore their surroundings in their mind's eye: *How does it look? What sounds can you hear? Are there scents in the air? What is the temperature and weather? How does your body feel while you're here? Are there any people or animals around? What else can you describe?* We can incorporate this information into a script and/or recording that can be utilized during visits and in the active dying process.

Is it closure work?

In our role as listener, doulas invite clients to bring intrusive or suppressed thoughts and memories to the surface. We become a safe person clients know they can trust with disclosures. A doula is a sounding board. Clients might feel nervous to say something aloud, but they can practice with us. When asked, doulas can mediate difficult conversations between people, holding the deeper meaning of resolution in our minds, encouraging all included to listen with open hearts. We can process with each person separately afterward, continuing our role as an unbiased third party. Clients might want to offer forgiveness, request forgiveness, express love and gratitude, or say goodbye. Doulas can help arrange and support this closure work.

Is it meaning-making?

Doulas feel honored to hear people's stories. We cherish this special time of honesty and sharing. As clients tell about their jobs, relationships, adventures, disappointments, accomplishments, and lessons learned, we know they are sorting, assessing, and making meaning of their time on Earth. Doulas can offer to become scribe, writing or recording what clients impart. This is sacred work. We remain nonjudgmental in our expressions, body language, tone, and wording. We believe each of us has lived a life worth validating.

Is it legacy work?

Legacy gifts come in many forms. They are as unique as each person's life. A doula can work with a client to create projects that appeal to them specifically. Jewelry, scrapbooks, journals, diaries, videos, letters, heirlooms, and cookbooks are some ideas. Clients may enjoy the process of creating the legacy project (because it is a time of thoughtful reflection), and the fulfillment of having completed a project that will become a lasting treasure for the recipient(s). Depending on a client's energy level, this work will require more or less direct effort from the doula and may span a number of visits.

Is it planning?

Doulas can assist in documenting each client's values-based wishes for care—specifying each client's hopes, beliefs, and requests. During visits, we discover religious or spiritual practices, and preferences for music, readings, and ceremonies, which become the foundation for concrete plans.

Doulas can help clients complete their advance directives. We can ask: *What are your priorities for your care? Who is your chosen health care proxy?* Through this communication, we encourage informed consent, because we acknowledge the importance of active involvement in decision-making. We promote a client's sense of agency and build a better understanding of client preferences for times when we can no longer ask questions. Together, we explore the options of living wakes, burials (home, green, or traditional), funerals (home or at a venue), cremation, remembrances, memorials, and celebrations of life. We can help create rituals for these sacred rites of passage, as well. There are myriad opportunities for creative personalization.

Is it connecting clients to resources?

A doula needs to have a comprehensive directory of relevant offerings available to clients. When a task falls outside of a doula's scope or specific care package, we can provide clients with contact details for hospice and palliative care teams, spiritual care providers, counselors, support groups, complementary care practitioners, celebrants, funeral guides and homes, crematoriums, cemeteries, and so forth.

We always offer opportunities and suggestions without attachment to the outcome. Doulas trust that clients know what's best. Even when we're quite certain that a particular choice might ease suffering, we do not push an agenda. We understand that our client's right to having a voice usurps all. Also, we recognize that wisdom arises organically through a process of discovery; it cannot be transmitted from one person to another. True catharsis cannot be forced.

Is it care coordination?

Doulas oversee the broad picture of client care, to assess its completeness and level of organization. We consider a client's network of support, including the medical team (likely hospice or palliative care), loved ones, friends, neighbors, and community members—in addition to resources utilized from our directory lists. We recognize the unparalleled contributions of doctors, nurses, aides, chaplains, social workers, and therapists. We also evaluate the nonmedical team. The goal is for everyone involved to operate within their comfort zone. What are people's strengths? How can we "plug them in" accordingly to construct a cohesive plan?

Doulas can create calendars with appointments and visits that honor the client's energy level and desires for their time. We can make a simple sign outside a client's space, defining their wishes. For example:

Please leave your worries, keys, shoes, and distractions (devices) at the door. Enter as yourself. Don't worry about saying the wrong thing. I want time with you. See me as the person you've known. Add a special memory to my notebook and share it aloud.

Is it vigil sitting?

A vigil is a sacrosanct time of transition that commences when a client begins the active dying phase and continues through the end of life. A client is no longer communicative (for the most part) and spends much of the time in a deep sleep. Doulas are often included in a client's vigil. We will likely have helped develop a vigil plan ahead of time by getting to know our client and asking clarifying questions:

Where would you like to be? Who would you like surrounding you? What smells are comforting to you (essential oils, fresh flowers, cookies baking, soup cooking)? What songs or nature sounds soothe you? Would you like prayers, excerpts, or poems to be read?

Are there sacred objects and mementos we can arrange? How do you feel about touch (gentle massage, hand holding) and embrace? Do you prefer peace and quiet or the noise of gatherings? Have you made your wishes for medications known to your team? How would you like your body to be cared for afterward (washing, anointing, dressing in chosen garb or a shroud, viewings, time spent undisturbed, rituals)?

Soul's Eye View

Doulas regularly monitor the big picture. This vantage goes beyond merely engaging our brains, as our logic is limiting in this realm. It goes beyond our emotional center because feelings can blur our neutrality. A soul's eye view is expansive and includes balanced awareness from our minds and doula hearts—the practical and the emotional.

Since we are slightly removed from the inner circle of care and concern, we can step back and survey the entirety. We notice how different figures are operating. Who's upset? Who's isolating themselves? Who's taking on the role of martyr? Who's present? How are they affecting one another? Doulas recognize that energies are colliding and feelings are constantly in flux.

Doulas carefully consider how we fit into the care team. Is a social worker already drafting funeral plans with the family? Is the hospice chaplain or priest from the client's church meeting regularly to discuss existential questions? Would an aunt love to organize the creation of a giant photo collage? Is there a brother who feels compelled to manage the appointment and visitor schedule? Doulas don't duplicate. We note care gaps and fill them as needed. No two clients will require the same exact level and type of doula support.

Doulas have numerous jobs, activities, exercises, and techniques to administer, but we are also there as a companion, witness, and listener. This requires graceful flexibility. Meeting people where they are means not always adhering to a premeditated itinerary. We need to be versatile and adaptable while remaining within our scope.

Self-Care While Caregiving

The end of life is a turbulent time that asks much of everyone involved. Loved ones can easily become exhausted and burnt-out. Doulas can promote self-care by encouraging approaches that preserve well-being. Self-care isn't selfish; it's necessary. The times we feel we have the least energy to put toward self-care are precisely the times we need it most.

During visits, doulas can inquire: *How are you doing? Really doing?* We look beyond any obvious, outward signs of functioning, past the rote response of "fine," and aim the question toward their likely state of disequilibrium: *Are you getting rest? Have you eaten? Would you like to get some fresh air?*

Caregivers might question: *How can I think about eating when ___ can't any longer? How can I enjoy the smell of spring blooms when lilacs were ___'s favorite? I'm far too busy to tend to my needs with all of these tasks and logistics to figure out.*

Doulas explain that people must make time to care for themselves—for their own sake, as well as their loved ones'. It's a vital practice that will result in more sustainable energy levels. When our cups are empty, we have nothing to give. When we feel guilty about filling our own cups, everyone suffers. Doulas suggest caregivers take a nap or go for a walk, meet a friend for coffee, see a movie, or get a massage.

Doula Language

In all communication, doulas must be mindful of tone and the words we choose. We meet people where they are. We take into account not only their emotional state, views, practices, and preferences, but also seek to honor their vernacular. Do they have a nickname for their condition? Or for a tumor, perhaps? Do they call cancer "the big 'C'"? Do they say the word "death," or avoid it entirely? Some people remain in absolute denial of their condition, and others might not be willing to use clear language. A person can be "passing," or "gone." We can "lose" someone, or sometimes a person has "left" us. There are many euphemisms and references that replace direct, unfiltered terminology, and their use is prevalent in our largely death-phobic culture. With compassion, we notice and understand this inclination.

Client Doula Versus Advocacy Doula

When working with clients, our ability to adopt their preferred language fosters connection and becomes a way to show respect. We do not enter with an agenda, seeking to change anyone or convince them they're wrong. We know that, at any point, a client might feel ready to say a weighted, feared word aloud, but we understand that it must be on their own terms in order to feel valid to them. This is the appropriate, nonjudgmental stance of a "client doula."

Many end-of-life caregivers feel compelled to raise awareness and encourage open conversations about the dying process as advocates of the changing tide. Outside our visits with clients, we may want to utilize more candid language to challenge taboos and myths. We can break down stereotypes about how "morbid" and "depressing" this work is. We can share how uplifting and inspiring it is to face our mortality.

We wake up! We live fully! We remember not to take people or moments for granted. We find more peace, more joy, and we lighten our loads of unfinished business regularly by not falling into procrastination traps.

As advocacy doulas, we have much to accomplish. As client doulas, we must take heed.

Opting In or Opting Out

Doulas always ask for permission and consent when offering suggestions. This can include something seemingly unimportant like asking, "Why don't I move that chair out of the way of visitors and put it by the window so that your space has better flow?" Or, it could be a more pressing issue such as saying, "You always have to call to your husband to have him hand you a drink. Why don't we set a water bottle in your chair with you so it's nearby?" However, maybe that chair was there so that the client could see the birds visiting at the feeder and you've inadvertently blocked the view. Or maybe the wife wants to have reasons to call her husband near her and her husband likes feeling useful, but they don't feel comfortable verbalizing this dynamic. In both cases, the wording of the questions has required the client to "opt out" by refusing. This can place the client in an awkward position. They may not want to disappoint or be thought of as difficult or selfish.

Instead of requiring clients to decline offers, we can approach with curiosity and formulate "opt in" opportunities. "I noticed the chair in front of the doorway. Is there a special reason you have it there?" "I noticed you often call to your husband when you're thirsty. Let me know if you'd like a water bottle in your chair. I'm happy to get one for you." We leave space for discussion and discovery, and from there, we can find amicable solutions that honor the core yearnings of the client.

When we're engaging in touch of any sort, permission is paramount. We might wonder if a client would enjoy a hand massage or foot rub, or would like to have their hair gently brushed. These are intimate acts of caring. They require trust, vulnerability, and an expressed interest from the client. Even holding a hand can feel intrusive to some. Doulas can make standing offers. "I see you're clenching your fists today. Let me know if you'd like a hand massage." Or, "I'm going to leave my hand here on the side of the bed if you'd like to hold it. It's entirely up to you."

This "opt-in" approach is so crucial because we recognize that clients lose control over many areas of their life as they navigate the progressive losses of physical abilities, roles, and independence. We want to provide as many chances as possible for clients to make their own choices. We do not make guesses because we can't be certain how an idea will be received even after we've established a strong relationship. We don't want to risk having a client appease us by withholding their true opinion. Clients need to know they won't let us down, that our egos won't be bruised. We focus on empowering, not directing.

Preparatory Grief Support

A doula's main focus is on the client. Inclusion of loved ones, however, is an integral part of providing holistic support. A client's sense of tranquility may be partly based on whether they believe their loved ones will carry on without them: *Will they be okay? Will someone take care of them?*

End-of-life doulas can help families develop wishes for this often overwhelming time. Just as a birth doula inquires about an expectant family's postpartum plans, an end-of-life doula can inquire about a post-passage plan. We can ask: *What expectations do you have? What might help you feel most cared for? What types of supports do you have in place and what can we consider arranging?*

These conversations require grace. Doulas need to recognize the appropriate moments to broach these topics—or, if a client's loved ones aren't ready, to plant seeds for future talks. Minimizing surprises helps enhance people's sense of confidence as they enter into the unknown. We can alert people to what commonly occurs, nurturing foresight and readiness. Preparation tempers the impact and influence of unsolicited "help."

Preparing for What's Possible

We are all touched by death and thus we are all connected within its web. Pain and sadness are universal. Generally, when people convey condolences, they do so with sincerity. However, even well-intentioned words can be unhelpful and sometimes even hurtful. People often wonder what to say and what not to say.

Well-Intentioned but Misguided

People are naturally curious. But when they ask how the dying experience unfolded, they're placing a burden on the bereaved, who might not be ready to speak about the events leading up to or following the death. They might feel exhausted and unable to formulate articulate sentences or make meaning. People may think they're creating space for processing, but that has to happen on the mourner's terms—their timing, their choice. Sharing needs to be for the benefit of the mourner, not to satisfy the curiosity of the listener.

Conversely, grief can be quite isolating. People might avoid the topic completely (even when a bereaved individual brings up their loss), because they want to spare the mourner the pain of rehashing and reliving the experience. They shut down openers to any conversation about the death in an effort to protect the mourner (as well as themselves, perhaps).

How can supporters find an appropriate balance? We can create compassionate space for processing to occur without pressure by extending an invitation: *I'm here to listen if you'd like to talk.*

Platitudes and Stock Phrases

"At least he is not in pain." "She is in a better place." "It will get better with time." "God only gives you what you can handle." "Heaven needed an angel."

We've all heard them. They sound almost soothing. These phrases have the potential to be comforting when, and only when, they come from the bereaved themselves. Such sentiments need to be arrived at organically through grieving. They won't resonate if they're forced.

Grieving is a process—a messy, unpredictable process, unique for each person and each loss. We cannot drag someone through their grief. Mourners hold the maps to their own healing paths. They are meant to lament, struggle, reminisce and accept in their own way—and they need others to be open-minded and open-hearted. The most welcomed words of support tend to be those which require the least amount of effort in response from the mourner.

Comparing and Commiserating

"You should…" "You should never…" "When ___ died, I ____." "Make sure to ____, it worked wonders for me."

In order to help the bereaved feel they're not alone, sometimes people are tempted to overlay their own stories of heartache. Instead of listening and allowing space for silence or processing, they might feel the need to fill the pauses with words of wisdom or tales of their own. This doesn't leave adequate room for the person who is grieving to find their own way toward healing. Even more harmful, shifting this focus might make mourners feel obligated to console others. People deep in grief often just want some company as they sit in the emotional space of their choosing. They won't be ready for a hand up until they're ready.

Doulas recognize that when we're supporting the bereaved, it is not the time to unearth our own unresolved baggage. At the same time, we acknowledge that we may be triggered by a smell, a sound, or a sight that propels us to another time and place in our memory. We can notice this happening and put it aside temporarily. In the back of our mind, we can set an intention to attend to it when we've finished our visit. To do our work well, we need to prioritize self-care by regularly evaluating and processing our "stuff."

By preparing clients and their loved ones for these various types of unhelpful remarks and unsolicited advice, doulas empower them to receive or deflect messages, removing the obligation to accept and integrate what doesn't resonate. We assuage any lack of confidence they might experience: *What works for you will be unique to you.*

Practical Help

Bereaved individuals tend to appreciate support that goes beyond "What can I do?" A life-altering loss often ushers in brain fog—an inability to think clearly, even about one's basic needs (hydration, nourishment, sleep) and threatens one's capability to keep up with tasks such as cleaning, bills, and appointments. Doulas can offer suggestions for how to navigate the logistics of daily life, from self-care practices to simple list-keeping habits. A list can include current to-dos, like household chores, pet care, errands, sorting mail, and grocery items.

People sometimes revere stoic autonomy. They feel weak asking for help. They were taught to buck up and carry on. Due to this pressure, people stifle their feelings and pretend to function by relying on distractions, over-scheduling, numbing-out, or medicating. Grief becomes heavy emotional baggage until mourners find the courage to unpack it. To begin healing, people need to turn toward pain and suffering. Surrendering to grief is a choice.

Doulas affirm that true strength comes from being honest—honest about doubts, needs, and interdependence. We encourage: *You can accept help; you can lean on your village.* Having a list enables people to say "yes, thank you" without shame or guilt when offers are truly beneficial. Instead of thinking up an answer on the spot, a mourner can simply point to the list and express how lovely it would be to cross off one to-do.

Just as embracing the grieving process is vital, the experience of providing support can be vital for those surrounding the bereaved.

Doulas can help a client's loved ones formulate responses that best answer the common question: *How can I help?*

- Honor my loss
- Speak the name of my loved one
- Share a memory
- Hold my hand
- Make our family a meal
- Sit in silence

Drift and Rift

Death leaves a great void in its wake—one that often becomes more pronounced during times of annual traditions. What's missing becomes glaringly noticeable. The year of "firsts" is often thought of as the most arduous, with all the birthdays, anniversaries, and holidays. It's not uncommon for families to struggle and squabble in their discomfort. Facing a special moment without the person who died can feel insurmountable. Family members might quarrel or even avoid gatherings when togetherness would likely provide comfort. Avoidance keeps grief at a distance.

This often happens at a very subconscious level. Doulas can prepare clients' loved ones ahead of time. What's the alternative? Drawing close. Acknowledging the pain. Leaning on one another. Talking, sharing, crying, embracing, and supporting. We encourage those grieving to reinvent traditions and consider new rituals and remembrances.

Ghosting

Loss infiltrates all realms, affecting a person's sense of self and each of their relationships to varying degrees. Hardship can bring people together or tear them apart. Some people from a mourner's "village" will step up and step in. Others will disappear, or "ghost." While this behavior seems unjust, adding insult to injury when the bereaved have already endured significant loss, ghosting generally stems from fear. People might worry they won't know how to relate because they don't know what to say or how to help. They might feel hesitant to be in close proximity to another's heartache. In short, they feel overwhelmed.

Doulas draw closer when others back away. We are steadfast. When providing post-passage care, we remain present and engaged. Yet, doulas are not family members or friends. We are acting in a professional capacity and are not limitlessly available. It's important for clients and their loved ones not to become overly dependent on our company as this would undermine their sense of self-efficacy. Part of a doula's responsibility, then, is to recognize when to move in and when to step back, allowing clients to summon their own strength.

In anticipation of this stage, doulas help people identify and build their natural support systems. We encourage clients to consider: *Who is a go-to? Who can you call on?* Also, a doula might proffer additional resources at this time, including a grief counselor and/or support groups.

Life Beyond Loss

Doula as Story-Listener

After the funerary arrangements and practical tasks have been completed and the reality of grief sets in, a doula returns for a post-passage visit with a client's loved one(s). It's important to plan this meeting once the dust has settled. We explain that we'd like to check in and talk about our time together. We need to gauge their level of readiness for this communication. This can be a poignant time of reflection, discovering beauty found in the journey.

During the visit, doulas notice and support the emotional health and well-being of our client's loved ones. We ease our presence back into their space, knowing that enormous changes have occurred, making no assumptions about how their loss has or hasn't been integrated. With our beginner's minds engaged, we create space for a check-in and review. Just as a birth doula visits a new family during the postpartum period to assess their transition, an end-of-life doula checks on a client's family's "new normal" and provides an opportunity for processing.

- How have you been doing? What does an average day look like lately?

These answers shed light on this early phase of grief. Are they sleeping? Eating? Socializing? Beginning to assimilate?

- In your words, can you share the story of ___'s death/passing (inserting their vernacular)?

This provides an invaluable opportunity for loved ones to recount their experience of the dying process. As they retell the story from their point of view, doulas draw out thoughts and feelings so they're not suppressed, helping to avoid unhealthy patterns of rumination. Such conversations promote greater clarity by piecing together what happened. We help combat perceptions of alienation by supporting those grieving.

- What were the most meaningful or impactful moments for you?

Doulas accept that explanations will be unorganized and thoughts will be scattered. We follow the loved one's lead, allowing them to guide the direction of the conversation. When we notice heightened emotions surrounding particular memories, we spend extra time exploring those depths—to the extent desired. Cues include tears, poignant pauses, and marked expressions. We look for signs of guilt or remorse and encourage cathartic release through communication. "We're human. You're human. It was a difficult time. We do the best we can," we remind them as they air what feels unresolved.

- What was most difficult? Most surprising?

As loved ones contemplate their journey, they become aware of possible lessons learned and gifts bestowed. We ask: *What might you share with others?* This is a way to reaffirm their strength, however clouded and doubtful they might seem at the moment.

- Do you feel ___'s wishes were honored?

This prompt can bring up points of contention. Were there arguments amongst family members or disagreements about medical care? Can we can help sort through any miscommunication? Were there elements of the dying person's advance directives or vigil plan that weren't carried out due to circumstances beyond our control?

What went well? A doula can point out examples of how the client's wishes were revered. Our soul's eye view affords us a more all-encompassing vantage point, in contrast to a loved one who is naturally consumed by the closeness of their relationship. A doula might have noticed meaningful moments that went unseen by others. The dying person might have given the doula special messages to pass on, as well. These recollections can often be very moving when shared.

At the conclusion of the loved one's narrative, doulas review the main points of the story, noting examples of courage, connection, and love, while offering genuine praise for what brings the loved one most pride. With sincerity, we acknowledge their struggle, their choices, and their resilience.

At this point, the doula can extend an invitation for a loved one to reminisce about the person who died and express anything left unsaid. Sometimes sentiments are withheld for fear of upsetting those included or due to a depth of sadness that silences. A doula can listen as a client's loved one speaks from the heart.

We can ask:

- What memory of ___ do you hold most dear?
- What did you love/like/respect/cherish most about ___?
- What made ___ unique/special in your eyes?
- Was there anything you meant to say (but didn't) that you'd like to share?

Lastly, we ask about life beyond loss:

- What are you doing to care for yourself? What are your plans for the next few months?

Are they able to see themselves moving forward, or are they paralyzed by grief? At varying levels of consciousness, survivors often feel guilty for continuing to live—for "moving on" without the person who died. Guilt can develop a strong hold on many moments and choices following a loss. Letting go of the pain might seem to threaten their love, connection, and commitment to the one they lost. A doula is in a position to pose some difficult yet liberating questions: *Can loved ones open to joy once more? Can they begin to consider that the living are meant to live fully? Can they imagine the scenario reversed (i.e., they had died instead) and consider how they would want a loved one to engage with the world? Can they perhaps aspire to heal in honor of the departed?*

To reach closure within the doula/client relationship, we express our gratitude for having been invited to support. We acknowledge the gifts bestowed upon us, wisdom gleaned, and how our hearts were touched by bearing witness.

Self-Care While Grieving

Mourning requires physical, emotional, and mental energy. Part of self-care is accepting support from others, and part of it is carving out time for activities that feed a person's soul. Doulas can encourage mourners to make sure their basic needs are met, and to take some time to engage in an interest.

People sometimes describe grief as akin to an injury or wound. There can be physical manifestations—feelings of a broken heart, a crushing sensation in the chest, a knot in the pit of the stomach. Initially the pain of grief can feel all-consuming, leaving mourners struggling to get by, minute-to-minute. Upon waking in the morning or perhaps for a fleeting moment during the day, a mourner might forget the loss before the reality returns with its crushing weight and power. As time passes, those brief respites from the initially unrelenting pain occur more frequently and gradually last longer. Mourners find themselves getting by hour-to-hour and then day-by-day.

When the bereaved find themselves smiling and even laughing, they often feel ashamed for being happy without the person who died. They question: *How can I enjoy life without my partner/parent/friend?* The sharp sting of the agony gently eases ever so slightly to make space for a new normal—for adjusting.

How does a heart survive such sorrow? Not without doubt. Not without feelings of hopelessness and despair. A heart survives by expanding around the grief. People don't "get over it." Healing means integrating loss into the mind and finding a new way of being in the world. The loss remains an unshakable memory, forever housed inside us. Yet, as we take timid steps, our hearts begin to grow outward beyond the space inhabited by the sadness. New experiences, new connections, new opportunities for joy widen our capacity for happiness. "Moving on" means honoring our grief and bravely opening ourselves to what's to come.

Doulas can help prepare a client's loved ones for this process by illuminating their natural coping strategies that are already established. We can inquire: *Tell me about a difficulty you navigated in your life. How did you deal with it? What helped you feel strong?*

All humans stumble and trip during life. We learn more from adversity and our (perceived) failures than our successes. We find out what we're made of. We realize who we can count on in times of need. As doulas enter into this space, we help people realize their fortitude. We hold faith in the strength of each individual, even when they cannot recognize it in themselves.

A doula, with steady rootedness, naturally becomes a balm for suffering, because we trust that people will not shatter when broken-hearted. Each of us is equipped with all the pieces needed to rebuild. The new version won't be an exact replica; it's infused with grit born of struggle and insight discovered through the brave work of healing.

"Grief can be the garden of compassion. If you keep your heart open through everything, your pain can become your greatest ally in your life's search for love and wisdom." -Rumi

A Sit with M.

I find my breath
Guilty? or Grateful?
I check for signs of yours
Lucky? or Lingering?

I see, in your tired eyes
-which I wipe with dampened cloth-
Yearning

I feel, in your shaking hand
-which I hold gently in mine-
Restlessness

I hear, in your muted sounds
-which I strain to comprehend-
Love

I sit as Doula
I sit as Human
I sit as Life, bright yet knowing
Witness to thresholds
present and still.

SECTION THREE

Contemplative Practice

"I hear and I forget. I see and I remember. I do and I understand."
-Confucius

It's one thing to study essentials of doula care; it's another to use them. Practice makes progress. Practice also confirms the effectiveness of doula approaches and techniques, and helps us build a reservoir of trust in this work. Here are a number of prompts to get you started and/or enhance your skills. Work through them alone or with a supportive group. Many of these are lifelong practices.

1) Open-Mindedness

Think of your most strongly-held belief. One that has an opposing view and could be debated. One that, when questioned, feels like an attack on your very personhood. Losing your grip on this belief feels threatening and scary.

Focusing on this belief, take a few minutes to meditate on these questions:

- Where did this belief come from and when did you adopt it?
- What's at the core of this belief?
- What virtues are attached to it?

Now that you have a clear vision of your belief, imagine the extreme opposite viewpoint. What would it be?

Focus on this opposing belief and take a few minutes to meditate on the same questions as before, except this time, attempt to open your mind to the "other" side without judgment. Ask yourself:

- Where might this belief have come from?
- What might be at the root of this belief?
- What virtues might be attached to it?

Doulas will encounter people who have different opinions. Hot button issues like politics, religious contentions, and social movements will arise during our work. We want clients to feel invited to express themselves without fear of judgment, cultivating space for deeper work. We cannot react to triggers by challenging or berating. We must remain curious and open: *That sounds very important to you. Can you tell me more?*

Arguably, the most difficult ego work doulas face is leaving their agenda at the door when entering a client's space. We enter as "client doula," not "advocacy doula." Any righteousness or dogmatic pleas must remain outside of this work. Can we hold our views quietly in our hearts as we listen to varying voices? Can we trust that our ideals need not be heard and understood by clients to be personally revered? Any internal discomfort we feel in response to a client's communication is ours and ours alone. Our responsibility. Our work. It stems from needing to continually practice humility and signals a cue to process during self-care time.

We cannot argue our truths while acting as doula. We are respectful visitors, honored to witness and support without judgment. A client's "home" (be it their owned/rented property, a hospital room, or residential placement) is their safe space, where they can be themselves and speak freely, and where they deserve to be treated with dignity always.

Neutrality and genuine curiosity generally de-escalate any anger that might flare up. However, if a doula feels personally accosted or threatened, then it is appropriate to cease involvement with that client. For professional doulas, it is important to include language in your written contract that covers such cases.

2) Silent Listening

Find a volunteer who is willing to help you practice silent listening. Meet in a quiet space free from interruptions. Sit comfortably. Let your volunteer know you'd like them to share a special memory, one you may or may not have been involved in or heard before. Tell them you want to hear the whole story with as much detail as possible, and let them know it's okay to go off course and talk about other thoughts that come to mind. Let them know that you won't be speaking, only listening. Set a timer for five minutes and put it aside, out of sight. Give your volunteer a nod to begin and then enter into your intentional presence as story-listener.

- Hear with your ears, your mind, your eyes, and your doula heart.

- Do not talk or take notes—and limit your nods, expressions, and noises to a minimum.
- Hold a soft gaze.
- If you lose focus, re-center by finding your breath and sense of curiosity.
- Free yourself from the demands of formulating responses.

When the timer goes off, encourage your volunteer to wrap up any final thoughts. Then, reflect together. How was that? Uncomfortable or comfortable? Awkward? Pleasant? Too long or too short? How did your volunteer feel? How did you feel?

Although doulas are able to respond to clients verbally, we need to be vigilant about when and why we are talking. Who is it benefitting? Is it just to be heard? Is it to sound wise? Is it to push an agenda? Ask yourself: *Are you comfortable with silence?* Doulas must honor pauses and recognize the introspection that can occur during quiet moments. Finding ease within silence takes practice.

3) Unconditional Positive Regard

Think of a person you regularly communicate with and who counts on you for advice. This person turns to you during a crisis or when facing a challenge. They respect your opinion and say they always feel better after talking with you. They count on you. They hold your suggestions in high esteem. They might even feel lost without you.

Take some time to think about your role of "sage" in their eyes. How does this feel? Why do you feel compelled to help this person? Be honest with yourself. Do you feel wise or strong? Do you feel useful, needed, and fulfilled?

Now shift into a deeper contemplation. How do you view the other person? Maybe a bit weak? A little lost or confused? Helpless, perhaps? Someone in need of rescuing? This dynamic is very common and naturally occurs in many types of relationships. It comes from pure intentions. We don't want others to suffer needlessly. Yet, a power differential develops. The sage holds the answers and therefore the power.

What does it mean, instead, to be an ally? An *emotion ally*, an equal, a person who also stumbles and falls from time to time, feels overwhelmed in moments, and who doesn't always know the best steps forward. A person who doesn't claim to have all the answers to another human's questions.

How does this look? How might this sound?

Ponder this life example:

A teenager comes to their parent with a conundrum. They've gotten into two colleges and they're unsure about which one is best. Both colleges have the degree program that appeals most to the teenager. One is a two-hour drive from home and the other a plane flight away. How can a parent navigate this conversation?

The sage parent points out the pluses and minuses and shares their own story of lasting regret over choosing the wrong college. The sage parent feels very proud of helping their child through this complicated choice and for protecting them against the pain they endured.

In contrast, a parent with the doula heart recognizes our shared humanness and adopts the stance of a "mere mortal." This parent recognizes a mutual opportunity for growth and development. This parent asks the teenager: *What are the positives and negatives of both? What's your biggest fear? What's your most important goal? What is your gut telling you? What's the worst that could happen if you end up feeling like you made the 'wrong' choice?*

The mere mortal parent admits that even though adults make decisions all the time, they don't always feel like they know what they're doing. All humans struggle with the twists and turns of life. All humans can learn from mistakes as well as successes.

Ponder this doula work example:

A dying client wishes to reach out to a cousin after a decade-long estrangement. However, this reunion would likely make the client's partner very upset. What is a doula to do? The sage doula points out the pluses and minuses and shares an anecdote of a similar issue in which the reunion ultimately led to all parties feeling positive and grateful. The sage doula feels proud for telling the current client what the best path is and the client feels relieved to have an answer.

The mere mortal doula holds space while a client grapples with discomfort, surrenders to the murk, and sorts through the decision at their pace. Clarity may not come as a lightning-bolt epiphany. The resolution might not be miraculous. This doula never wavers, though. This doula assures the client: *This is really hard. There's no one right answer. I'm here. I'm listening, and I'm going to hold your hand as you struggle. I believe in you. No matter what decision you make, I will not judge you.*

The "sage" approach can lead to dependency and lack of confidence in the teenager/client, feeding the ego of the sage and depleting the sage of energy. When faced with challenges, the teenager/client doubts their innate capacity, so they turn outward for help. The "mere mortal" approach, while arguably more strenuous given its length of processing, leads the teenager/client toward feeling empowered. Moving forward, they tap into their inner wisdom and reach out to those who will companion, not lead. Likewise, the mere mortal's reserves remain full and perhaps even expand with the pride of witnessing another human find their way.

Practice this shift within relationships. How does it feel not to rescue people? Scary? Like you're letting someone down? Do you notice changes in the speaker? Are they upset with you for holding back your solutions? With trust, doulas relinquish a facade of control in favor of positive regard.

4) Suffering

Suffering is inevitable. We all have pain. We all deal with sadness, regret, guilt, and grief. Spend time writing about a heartbreak. Write down the story and all of your associated feelings, including the ones that bruise your pride. Peel back layers of emotional protection and expose any rawness that still resides. Write until it's all out of your system. Read over your piece and look for any new realizations, old patterns, or undiscovered truths.

Sit quietly in contemplation, holding yourself in unconditional positive regard, apologizing to and forgiving yourself and (perhaps) others. Acknowledge your humanness and how you did the best you could. Recall that we are all beautiful works in progress and that we're all connected by unavoidable pain and suffering. Either keep the writing for revisiting or burn it as a ceremonial sign of releasing yourself further into healing—whichever feels best to you.

5) Support

Think back through your life to a time when you felt truly supported. It could have been during a very trying time or a simpler exchange. Who was this person who held you so lovingly? What did this person do or say? What qualities did this person have? Do they align with doula essentials? How so? What can you develop and embody as a doula in honor of this support you received? What are your current strengths as a doula? What can you work on and practice?

6) Self-Preparation for Doula Work

In order to cultivate compassion and "walk the walk" of a dying person as genuinely as possible, doulas need to take time to complete our own advance directives, legacy projects, vigil plans, and farewell letters to loved ones. We can only present these completion tasks once we have approached them ourselves with humility and vulnerability. Revising and updating regularly is prudent!

Tenets of Doula Care

Doulas:

- Accept that birth, death, and grief are normal, natural, expected parts of life
- Provide non-medical, nonjudgmental emotional/spiritual support and soothing comfort measures
- Cultivate inner calm and peacefulness
- Promote informed consent for each client
- Gather relevant information and connect clients to beneficial resources
- Assist each client with having personally meaningful experiences—together developing wishes for care and encouraging the preservation of energy for what's most important
- Trust in the inherent wisdom of each client to discover their own best path
- Companion rather than treat
- Serve rather than fix
- Empower and encourage a client's loved ones to operate within their comfort zones, and fill in support gaps as they arise
- Promote self-care as vital to preserving and sustaining energy levels and enhancing holistic health

The "Ins" of Creating and Holding Space

1) Internal Shifts
- Grounding, centering, and slowing our pace
- Setting aside our to-do list, our day, and our worries
- Mindfulness and attentiveness

2) Intentional Presence
- Non-judgment and non-agenda
- Beginner's mind
- Genuine curiosity
- Witness, ally, and companion

3) Invitations
- Standing, welcoming invitations without attachment to the outcome/client's answer
- "Join me"
- "Be yourself here"
- "Feel safe and accepted here"
- Compassionate inquiry:
- "That sounds important to you. Tell me more"

4) Inclusion
- Living and dying are each a process in flux with shifting emotions, responses, and dynamics
- Understanding and acknowledging fluidity
- Responding with flexibility
- Welcoming it ALL and *being with*

Ode to an Iris

There are signs of strong roots as the breeze gently sways the perennial iris. Unflinching near the earth, the graceful oscillation builds upward, as does the colorful display. Off-shoots emerge from the sturdy, deep green foundation. Nearest the ground resides a tightly closed bud, perfect in its anticipation. Full of promise, it quietly awaits its turn in the sunny spotlight.

At its uppermost point, the stem reaches skyward in an unabashedly gorgeous bloom. Soft hues of yellow extend outward against a backdrop of purple speckles and stripes. Each shimmering petal stretches open, edges rolling back slightly in overextension, soaking in sun and exposing sweet nectar to bees, butterflies, and the occasional hummingbird. In the air wafts a deliciously potent aroma that echoes this essence of reaching its prime—the brief rapture of its peak.

Balanced in the middle of the stock, below the radiant blossom, rests a flower that was. Why does this urge arise to pluck it away? Does this sign of impermanence detract from the adjoining display of bright life? Why shouldn't both exist together, confirming the beauty of the crescendo in their affirmation of life's fleeting nature?

Is this aging flower shrinking and shriveling in misery? Is it slumped, saddened by decline? Perhaps not. Perhaps this elder bloom is peacefully resting, grateful and proud for having finished its work of beckoning pollinators, ensuring future seasons of growth.

It curls back into itself, gently hugging and creating a twist of color and texture, enveloping all memories of its brief existence. Is there humility in this graceful bow? Generosity? Is there work yet to be done? Wisdom to share? An aspiration to manifest contentment, conveying fertile trust in what is?

Acknowledgements

My heart is brimming with gratitude for so many who have held my hand and opened doors along the way.

To Sally MacFadyen for acknowledging my doula heart.

To Matt Sayre and Roberta MacDonald for entrusting the development of the UVM doula program curriculum to me. What an incredible privilege and journey.

I am much obliged to those who agreed to read this piece in draft form and provide such thoughtful, useful feedback, including Amy Sayre, Sara White, Lori Gurney, Charley MacMartin, and Dr. Robert Gramling.

A second debt of gratitude is owed to Dr. Gramling for inspiring a number of the doula essentials featured in the book, especially *beginner's mind* and *turning toward* as well as careful attention to language. Listening to you speak with such humility and reverence for your palliative care work helped me clarify my interpretation of end-of-life doula work.

To my over-worked editors, Heather Caulfield Mills, Jenny Wilkinson, and Jill Kiedaisch: *How did I manage to befriend such brilliant minds?!?* Thank you for turning my passionate ponderings into a coherent, logical read.

To my Haven families (doula clients) for inviting me into your most intimate, special moments. You've taught me what it means to be of service. I couldn't feel more honored.

To loved ones, friends, and supporters: *Thank you for believing in me and in the value of this message.*

Referenced Wisdom/Recommended Resources

Books:

Zen Mind, Beginner's Mind by Shunryo Suzuki

The Places That Scare You: A Guide to Fearlessness in Difficult Times by Pema Chödrön

Being with Dying: Cultivating Compassion and Fearlessness in the Presence of Death by Joan Halifax

On Death and Dying by Elisabeth Kübler-Ross

The Essential Rumi by Jalal al-Din Rumi and Coleman Barks

Making Friends with Death: A Buddhist Guide to Encountering Mortality by Judith L. Lief

Dying Well: The Prospect for Growth at the End of Life and *The Four Things That Matter Most* by Dr. Ira Byock

Websites:

National Hospice and Palliative Care Organization: nhpco.org

Advance Care Planning: fivewishes.org and starttheconversationvt.org

Center for Loss and Life Transition: centerforloss.com

University of Vermont Larner College of Medicine EOL Doula Professional Certificate Program: learn.uvm.edu/program/end-of-life-doula-certificate/

Contemplative Doula: Compassionate Heart, Curious Mind: contemplativedoula.com

Easing the Burden: mealtrain.com, lotsahelpinghands.com, caringbridge.org

"In this earth,
In this soil,
In this pure field,
Let's not plant any seeds
Other than seeds of
Love and Compassion" –Rumi

CPSIA information can be obtained
at www.ICGtesting.com
Printed in the USA
BVHW040314240721
612727BV00013B/1131